THE ROYAL HORTICULTURAL SOCIETY

Address Book

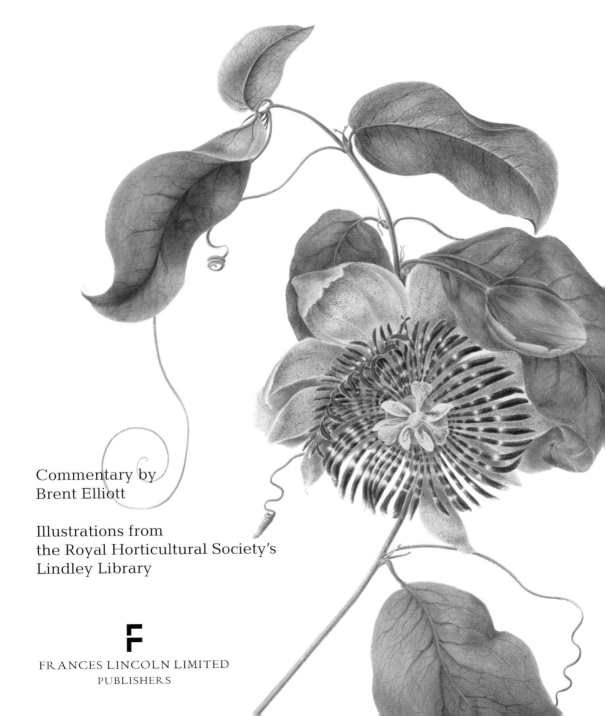

Commentary by
Brent Elliott

Illustrations from
the Royal Horticultural Society's
Lindley Library

F

FRANCES LINCOLN LIMITED
PUBLISHERS

Frances Lincoln Limited
4 Torriano Mews
Torriano Avenue
London NW5 2RZ
www.franceslincoln.com

Front Cover "Painted iris and summer
snowdrop": watercolour on vellum by James
Bolton (*c*.1735–99), depicting an extravagantly
patterned *Iris persica*, and *Leucojum aestivum*.
Back cover An elaborate but unnamed cultivar
of *Anemone coronaria*: watercolour on vellum
by an anonymous Italian artist, 17th or early
18th century.
Title page *Passiflora laurifolia*: watercolour
on vellum by Margaret Meen (fl.1775–1806),
dated 1785.

Introduction

Vellum, like parchment, was made from the skin of sheep, goat, or calf, but specially prepared by scraping and rubbing. It has been extensively used by artists as a medium for drawing.

Probably the oldest collection of drawings on vellum in the RHS collection is Italian in provenance, unattributed and undated, bound with the misspelled legend "FIORI BOTTAN" in gilt lettering on the spine. The drawings have been considered as 17th-century work, but the presence of a depiction of what is probably *Hippeastrum reginae*, a plant not known to have been introduced until the 1720s, suggests that they may be early 18th century instead.

Again, an album of six drawings on vellum by Claude Aubriet (1665–1742), which could have been compiled any time in the opening decades of the 18th century, has beautiful calligraphic labels and gilt borders. Aubriet was the first botanical artist to accompany a botanist on an expedition, and spent the latter part of his career as the official artist at the Jardin des Plantes in Paris. For these drawings, Aubriet used a mixture of watercolour and body colour – a dangerous technique for work on pages, for the pigment became brittle with age, and the turning of the leaves resulted in the flaking-off of portions of pigment.

In 1816 the Horticultural Society decided to honour its first Royal Patron and chose to have an artist prepare a decorated floral image on a sheet of vellum for the Queen to sign. Thus was inaugurated a tradition of Royal Autographs on vellum which has continued to the present day.

Even when not packaging their work for the elite, some botanical artists produced work on vellum. Georg Dionysius Ehret (1708–70), who became the most eminent botanical artist of the mid-18th century, produced much of his work for private patrons like the Duchess of Cavendish. Most of his work, even for such patrons, was on paper, but he drew some large pieces on vellum. His use of vellum may have been dictated purely by its effect on colours.

James Bolton (c.1735–99) is remembered today as the author of pioneering books on the ferns and fungi of Britain. In 1978 the RHS was bequeathed an album of drawings by Bolton, which included some specimens on vellum. He was also sponsored by the Duchess of Cavendish, but these drawings are small and unpretentious, and he probably used vellum for its aesthetic qualities.

Margaret Meen (fl.1775–1806) exhibited at the Royal Academy in the 1770s and 1780s, and published two parts of an intended work on *Exotic Plants from the Royal Gardens at Kew* in 1790. As with Ehret, the drawings are purely plant portraits with no decorative presentation.

Margaret Meen also taught drawing to others, including the four daughters of Joshua Smith, the Member of Parliament for Devizes (Emma, Eliza or Elizabeth, Augusta and Maria). Works by all four are held in the RHS Lindley Library and date from the 1780s.

The latest artist represented here is Pierre Jean François Turpin (1775–1840), an artist famous for the almost microscopic detail he put into his drawings. In 1820 Turpin and Poiteau published a work on plant anatomy and taxonomy called *Leçons de Flore*, and two copies of this work were specially printed on vellum, and the prints hand-coloured by Turpin.

Today, there has been a revival of interest in vellum. This address book gives a taste of the legacy of their predecessors.

Brent Elliott
Historian, RHS Lindley Library

Useful Addresses and Telephone Numbers

The purple wood sorrel, *Oxalis purpurea*: watercolour on vellum
by James Bolton (*c.*1735–99), dated 1793.

OXALIS *purpurea.*

J. Bolton pinxit. 1793.

A

A cultivar of *Anemone coronaria*: watercolour on vellum by an
anonymous Italian artist, 17th or early 18th century.

A

Rose, probably a cultivar of *Rosa centifolia*: watercolour on vellum
by James Bolton (*c.*1735–99).

J. Bolton pin
1791

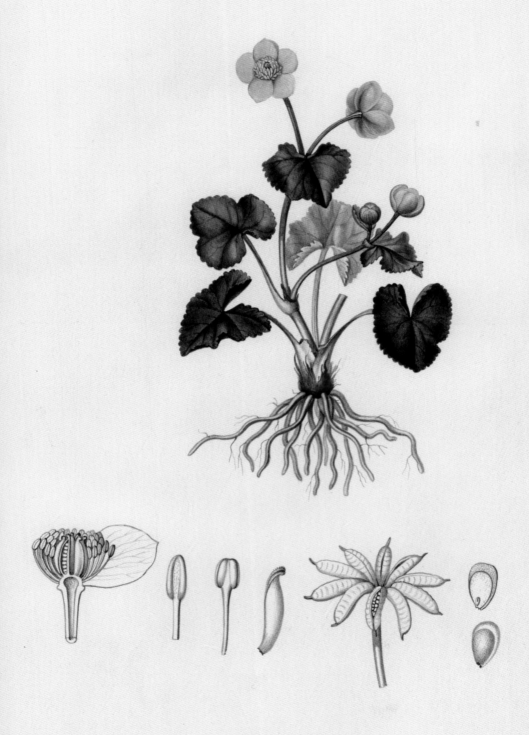

B

The marsh marigold, *Caltha palustris*: watercolour on vellum
by Pierre Jean François Turpin (1775–1840).

B

B

B

An elaborate but unnamed cultivar of *Anemone coronaria*: watercolour on vellum
by an anonymous Italian artist, 17th or early 18th century.

Monarda   *Punctata*   *Diandria Monogy*

C

The horsemint, *Monarda punctata*: watercolour on vellum
by Augusta Smith (fl.1780s–1845).

C

C

C

Narcissus tazetta subsp. *aureus*: watercolour on vellum
by an anonymous Italian artist, 17th or early 18th century.

D

The Virgin's bower, *Clematis viticella*: watercolour on vellum
by Emma Smith (fl.1780s–1845).

D

D

D

A peony of Spanish origin, *Paeonia lusitanica* (now *Paeonia broteri*):
watercolour on vellum by Maria Smith (d.1843).

Paonia lusitanica. Polyandria   Digynia   *Nr. 131*

E

The Turkey oak, *Quercus cerris*: watercolour on vellum
by Margaret Meen (fl.1775–1806), dated 1789.

E

E

E

The oleander, *Nerium oleander*: watercolour on vellum
by Augusta Smith (fl.1780s–1845).

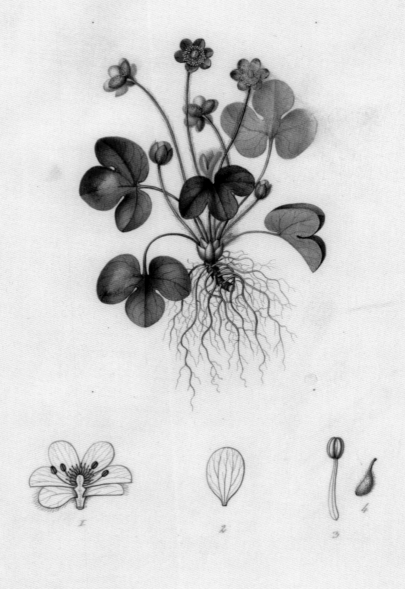

1   2   3   4

Turpin pinx.

ANÉMONE *hépatique.*

ANEMONE *hepatica.*

The hepatica, variously called *Anemone hepatica* or *Hepatica nobilis*: watercolour on vellum by Pierre Jean François Turpin (1775–1840).

F

F

F

The bat-winged passion flower, *Passiflora misera*: watercolour on vellum
by Margaret Meen (fl.1775–1806).

G

"Anemone latifolia calcidonia [sic = chalcedonica]", a doubled form of *Anemone coronaria*: watercolour on vellum by an anonymous Italian artist, 17th or early 18th century.

G

G

G

The globe flower, *Trollius europaeus*: watercolour on vellum
by Pierre Jean François Turpin (1775–1840).

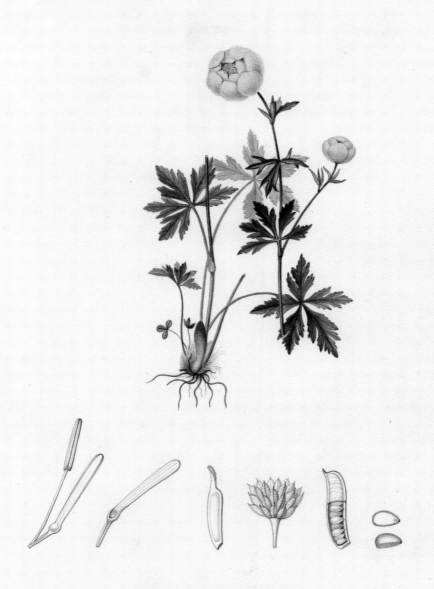

PERVAN·CARNEI·

·H·

H

"Peruan carnei", or the Portuguese squill (*Scilla peruviana*): watercolour on vellum by an anonymous Italian artist, 17th or early 18th century.

H

H

H

The coral tree, *Erythrina coralloides*: watercolour on vellum
by Eliza Smith (fl.1780s), dated 1785.

I

Lilium martagon, watercolour on vellum by an anonymous Italian artist,
17th or early 18th century.

I

The comparative anatomy of leaves: coloured illustration on vellum by
Pierre Jean François Turpin (1775–1840) from *Leçons de Flore* (1820).

TABLEAU X.

feuilles.

J

A cultivar of *Anemone coronaria* showing proliferation: watercolour on vellum
by an anonymous Italian artist, 17th or early 18th century.

J

The anatomy of fruits, in particular pods: coloured illustration on vellum
by Pierre Jean François Turpin (1775–1840) from *Leçons de Flore* (1820).

TABLEAU XXVI.
Fruits.

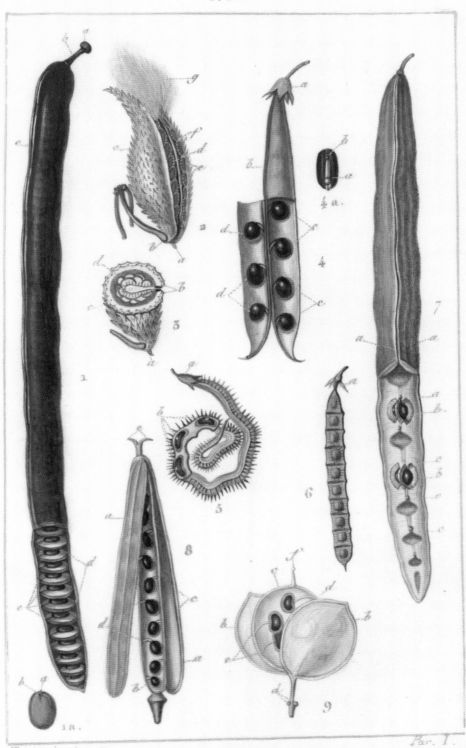

Turpin pinx.

A South African bulb, *Albuca altissima* (now, despite its country of origin,
Albuca canadensis): watercolour on vellum by Emma Smith (fl.1780s–1845).

K

TABLEAU II. (Bis)

Exemples de végétaux, tendant à prouver que le péricarpe n'est qu'une
sorte de nodus lacuneux, qui termine le système central des plantes (tige)
et qu'il peut dans certains cas continuer de s'allonger.

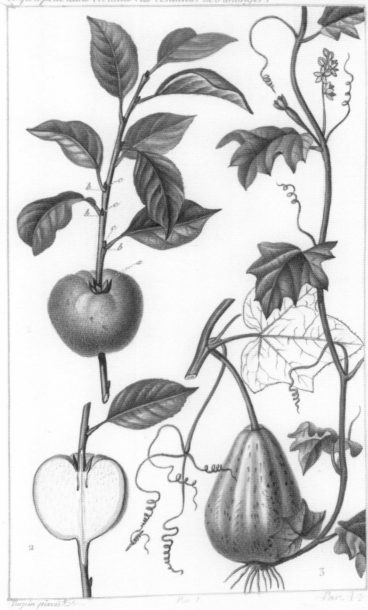

1 *POIRE* de crasanne. 2 *la même coupée verticalement*

3 *SECHIUM edule (Swartz)*

L

The anatomy of fruits: coloured illustration on vellum by Pierre Jean François Turpin (1775–1840) from *Leçons de Flore* (1820).

L

L

L

The castor oil plant, *Ricinus communis*: watercolour and body colour on vellum by Claude Aubriet (1665–1742).

Ricinoides arbor
Americana,
folio multifido.
I. r. h. 656.

A species of St John's wort, *Hypericum* sp.: watercolour on vellum
by Georg Dionysius Ehret (1708–70), dated 1757.

M

M

M

The Venus's fly-trap, *Dionaea muscipula*: watercolour
on vellum by James Bolton (*c*.1735–99).

A

DIONAEA muſcipula

J. Bol:

Two forms of *Narcissus tazetta*, one showing proliferation: watercolour on vellum by an anonymous Italian artist, 17th or early 18th century.

N

A South African bulb, "Gladiolus flavius nigro striatus", probably *Tritonia flabellifolia*: watercolour on vellum by Eliza Smith (fl.1780s).

1785. *Gladiolus flavus nigro striatus.*   *Triandria Monogynia.*

Ribes Americana, fructu nigre, minime,
Calyce floris Campani formi. Miller.

O

The American black currant, *Ribes americanum*: watercolour on vellum
by Georg Dionysius Ehret (1708–70), *c*.1765.

O

A wallflower, *Cheiranthus cheirii*: watercolour on vellum
by Pierre Jean François Turpin (1775–1840).

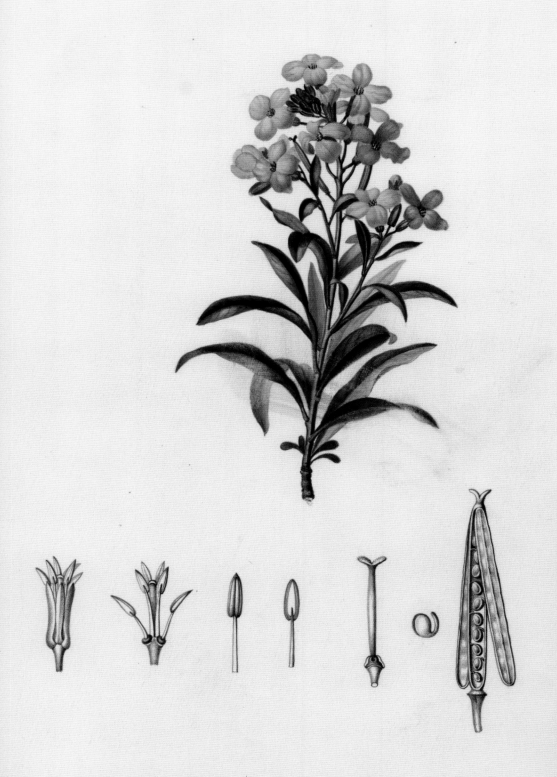

BUGLOSSUM

latifolium sempervirens. Bauh. pin

evergreen Alkanet.

Anchusa sempervirens. Lin.

G.D. Ehret. pinxit 17

Alkanet, *Pentaglottis sempervirens*: watercolour on vellum
by Georg Dionysius Ehret (1708–70), dated 1765.

P&Q

The common daffodil, *Narcissus pseudonarcissus*: watercolour on vellum by an anonymous Italian artist, 17th or early 18th century.

R

The black passion flower, *Passiflora vespertilio*: watercolour on vellum
by Margaret Meen (fl.1775–1806), dated 1787.

R

Yellow archangel, *Galeopsis galeobdalon*: watercolour on vellum
by Georg Dionysius Ehret (1708–70), dated 1757.

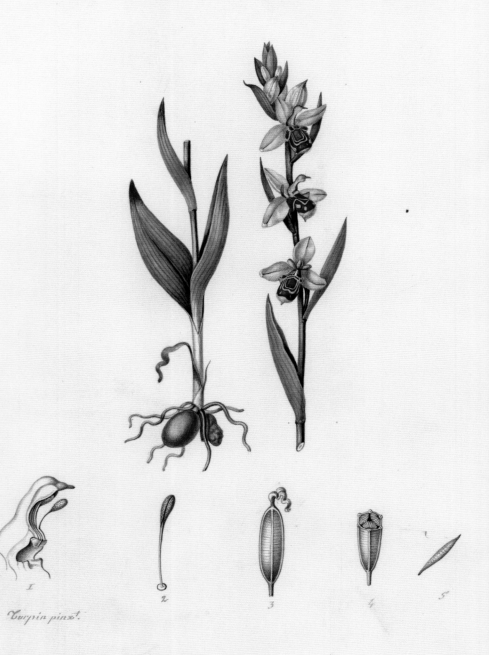

Turpin pinx.

1   2   3   4   5

OPHRYS *abeille*.

OPHRYS *apifera*.

The bee orchid, *Ophrys apifera*: watercolour on vellum
by Pierre Jean François Turpin (1775–1840).

S

S

S

The purple ragwort, *Senecio elegans*:
watercolour on vellum by Maria Smith (d.1843).

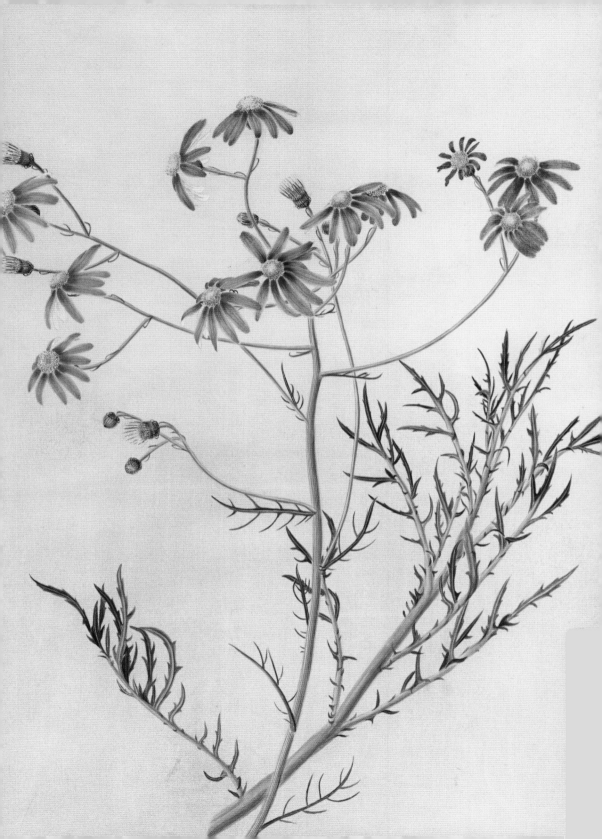

TABLEAU XXXI.

Fruits.

The anatomy of fruits, including melons and oranges: coloured illustration on vellum by Pierre Jean François Turpin (1775–1840) from *Leçons de Flore* (1820).

T

Anemone coronaria 'Flore Pleno': watercolour on vellum
by an anonymous Italian artist, 17th or early 18th century.

FLORE

TABLEAU XV.
Inflorescence.

Types of inflorescences: coloured illustration on vellum by Pierre Jean François Turpin (1775–1840) from *Leçons de Flore* (1820).

U &V

Tulip cultivar: watercolour on vellum by an anonymous Italian artist,
17th or early 18th century.

A foxglove, possibly *Digitalis lanata*, introduced in 1789: watercolour on vellum by Eliza Smith (fl.1780s).

W

The sea spurge, *Euphorbia paralias*: watercolour on vellum
by Georg Dionysius Ehret (1708–70), *c.*1764.

Gazania rigens, the first species of gazania to be introduced: watercolour on vellum by Eliza Smith (fl.1780s).

XYZ